Word Problems
The Language of Mathematics
A structured approach for children
in Key Stage 1 and Key Stage 2

by
Leonie Ewing and Ian Ward

A QEd Publication

Published in 2001
Reprinted in 2002

ISBN 1 898873 08 9

Published by QEd, The Rom Building, Eastern Avenue, Lichfield, Staffs. WS13 6RN
Web site: www.qed.uk.com
Email: orders@qed.uk.com

Leonie Ewing and Ian Ward work for the South-Eastern Education and Library Board Mathematics Department, Northern Ireland.

Printed in the United Kingdom by Stowes (Stoke-on-Trent).

Contents

Introduction

Word problems are perhaps one of the least popular and most difficult aspects of primary mathematics that children encounter. Often they can do the calculations – the mechanical aspect – but put the calculation into a written context and you will frequently hear, 'Is it an add or a take away?' showing uncertainty and a lack of confidence.

In order to help children who find word problems difficult and frustrating, this book takes a structured and varied approach to teaching the skills of solving word problems.

The earlier part of the book uses a pictorial approach and often involves a practical activity e.g. cutting and pasting the relevant word sentences to match the word problem. Later pages are intended for older children and extend the introduction of simple writing frames in order to provide a structured approach which is explained on page 47.

Why teach word problems step-by-step?

The step-by-step approach aims to help children gain confidence in their ability to successfully tackle word problems. It is important that children enjoy their experience of mathematics. Success in the early stages of learning helps children feel confident in their ability and confidence is vital if they are to continue to succeed. Decide on the pace that suits the individual child, giving additional work at the same level if required or indeed moving them on to the next step fairly rapidly. Gradually children will develop the feel for the structure and language of mathematical problems.

Classroom organisation

The activities in this pack can be completed individually or in pairs by children working together. The advantage of working together is that it requires children to think, discuss and reach joint decisions. Through discussing their work with their partner, the children have the opportunity to use mathematical language in context. Of course, children will vary in the amount of help they need to read the activity sheets. By working with a partner, the reading can be shared. As the children collaborate to complete the tasks, they are learning to co-operate, to help each other and consolidate their own thinking.

Using the worksheets

Many children who experience difficulties with number work find reading difficult as well. The pupil's sheets have been written using a limited vocabulary. Illustrations have been used to allow the children to work as independently as possible. However, pupils may still need some help in getting started. Use concrete materials as necessary according to the ability and understanding of the children. Encourage children to read the words before starting the activities and to use their individual Key Words and Word Lists (pages 116 and 117 – a list of basic key words for addition and subtraction are included for assistance). At each stage the children are encouraged to check their work after completion.

Using the Word List

Give each child a copy of the Word List on page 117 for their personal folder. Ask the child to colour in each picture when they first come across the word in a problem. Blank spaces have been included for children to add their own words as necessary.

Further ideas

1. Can children clarify mathematical ideas by talking and/or writing about them? The difficulty with most word problems is that they are artificial, so why not encourage children to write humorous, absurdly impossible word problems of their own, and by doing this not only foster links between mathematics and literacy, but also make them personal.

2. It is worth looking at a variety of word problems in which the solution is impossible to find from the data available. This was explored in an article in *Strategies* (Volume 5, Issue 1, Questions Publishing Company) 'How old is the Captain?', in which the author found that some primary pupils, when given six word problems *some of which were impossible to solve from the data given* within them, managed to find solutions to all six!

Here are the six problems:
1. Michael is 8 years old. His mother is 26 years older than Michael. How old is she?
2. Anke is 12 years old. Anke's mother is three times as old. How old is the mother?
3. A shepherd owns 19 sheep and 13 goats. How old is the shepherd?
4. A 27 year old shepherd owns 25 sheep and 10 goats. How old is the shepherd?
5. There are 13 boys and 15 girls sitting in a classroom. How old is the teacher?
6. A bee-keeper has 5 beehives with 80 bees each. How old is the bee-keeper?

Can this idea be used for further work, for example, children writing their own selection of word problems, only some of which can be solved?

Make a Word Problem

Children cut and paste sentences in order to make a word problem (illustrations are given for assistance).

Make a Word Problem

1   2   3

Put in order

1	
2	
3	

Cut and Paste

How many apples do Jack and Lucy have in total?

Jack found 3 apples .

Lucy found 5 apples .

Make a Word Problem

1   **2**   **3**

Put in order

1	
2	
3	

Cut and Paste

The cat ate 3 fish.

Lucy had 4 fish.

How many fish does she have left?

Make a Word Problem

| 1 | 2 | 3 |

Put in order

1	
2	
3	

Cut and Paste

How many buns are left?

There are 6 buns .

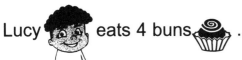Lucy eats 4 buns .

Make a Word Problem

1

2

3

Put in order

1	
2	
3	

Cut and Paste

He bought 2 more.

How many fish does he have altogether?

Jack has 5 fish in his tank.

Make a Word Problem

1

2

3

Put in order

1	
2	
3	

Cut and Paste

How many does she have altogether?

Jack gave her 7 more dinosaurs .

Lucy has 2 dinosaurs .

Make a Word Problem

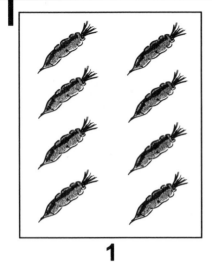

1

2

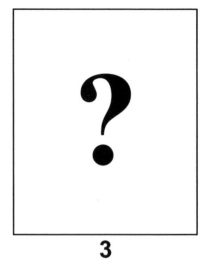

3

Put in order

1	
2	
3	

Cut and Paste

A rabbit  ate 5 carrots .

How many carrots are left?

There were 8 carrots  in the garden.

Word Problems

Draw It

Children cut and paste sentences in order to make a word problem.
Draw illustrations to match.
Children are encouraged to check their work after completion.

Draw It

Cut and Paste

How many apples 🍎 does he have altogether?

Jack has 5 apples 🍎.

Lucy gave him 3 more apples 🍎.

Put in order

1
2
3

• Check it •

Draw pictures for this calculation

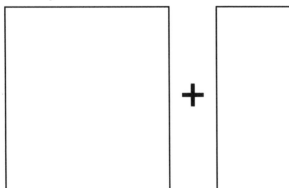

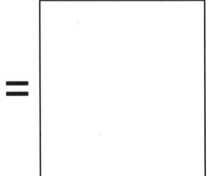

5 + 3 = 8

Draw It

Cut and Paste

6 aeroplanes at the airport.

How many aeroplanes are left?

4 aeroplanes  fly away.

Put in order

1	
2	
3	

• Check it •

Draw pictures for this calculation

| 6 | - | 4 | = | 2 |

Draw It

Cut and Paste

How many ghosts are left?

and 6 ghosts go away.

If there are 10 ghosts in the house

Put in order

1
2
3

• **Check it** •

Draw pictures for this calculation

	-		=	

10 - 6 = 4

Draw It

Cut and Paste

He lost 5 books .

How many books does Jack have now?

Jack had 10 books .

Put in order

1
2
3

• Check it •

Draw pictures for this calculation

	-		=	

10   -   5   =   5

Draw It

Cut and Paste

Jack put 5 cars 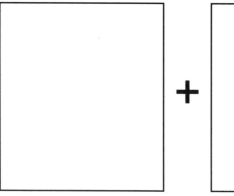 in the box.

Lucy put 4 cars  in the box.

How many cars 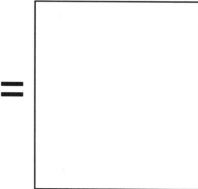 in total?

Put in order

1	
2	
3	

• Check it •

Draw pictures for this calculation

	+		=	
5	**+**	**4**	**=**	**9**

Draw It

Cut and Paste

How many ladybirds does this make altogether?

If Jack has 3 ladybirds and

Lucy has 5 ladybirds .

Put in order

1
2
3

• **Check it** •

Draw pictures for this calculation

3 **+** **5** **=** **8**

Draw It

Cut and Paste

She bought 3 more footballs .

Lucy has 4 footballs .

How many footballs in total?

Put in order

1	
2	
3	

• Check it •

Draw pictures for this calculation

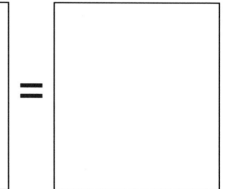

4 + 3 = 7

Draw It

Cut and Paste

2 butterflies fly away.

There are 8 butterflies in the garden.

How many are left?

Put in order

1	
2	
3	

• Check it •

Draw pictures for this calculation

8 - 2 = 6

Cut and Paste It

Children are given an illustration and a word bank of relevant words.
They are encouraged to construct their own word problems by cutting and pasting the word from Word Wall.

Cut and Paste It

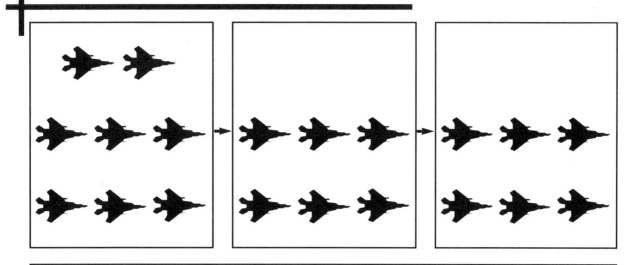

My word problem

• Check it •

Word Bank

| Two | Eight | . | left | ? | aeroplanes  | . |

| at the airport | aeroplanes | how many | are |

| fly away | | | |

Cut and Paste It

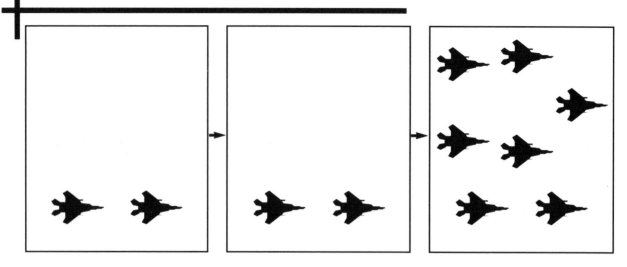

Word Bank

aeroplanes 	.	aeroplanes	Two	.
up in the sky	how many	more	come	Five
altogether	are	?	there	

Cut and Paste It

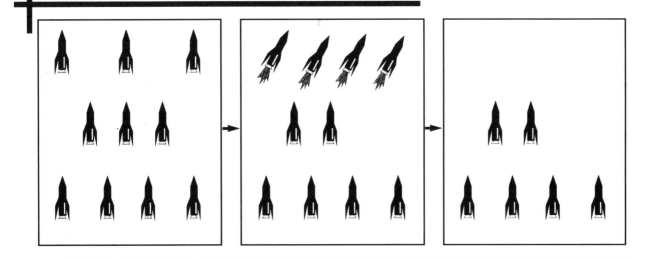

• Check it •

Word Bank

ten	There	.	are	?	rockets		Four
take off	.	How many	left	are	rockets	

Word Wall

Children are given Word Walls based on a variety of themes.
Using the given words and numbers they are encouraged to construct and check their own word problem(s).
Blank spaces are provided for any additional words required.

Word Wall – In the shop

Use these words to make up your own word problems.

I buy	sweets 	ice creams 	and
more	Then I buy	How many	sweets 
do I buy	altogether	in total	. .

How many do I have now?

How many do I have altogether? | ?

0	1	2	3	4	5	6	7
8	9	10					

Remember
You may have to change the capital letters

• Check it •

Word Wall – In the park

Use these words to make up your own word problems.

There are	playing	football 	children
on the swings		and	then	go home
more	come	How many	altogether
in total	are	left	.	?
0	1	2	3	4	5	6	7
8	9	10					

Remember
You may have to change the capital letters

• **Check it** •

Word Wall – At the bus stop

Use these words to make up your own word problems.

bus 	bus stop	children	get on
the	on the bus	There are	more	get off
the bus	How many children	are left	in total
How many children are on the bus now?	.	.
altogether	?	at	
0	1	2	3	4	5	6	7
8	9	10	

Remember
You may have to change the capital letters

• Check it •

Word Wall – At the airport

Use these words to make up your own word problems.

There are	aeroplanes		more	and
fly away	How many	left	are	airport
at	the	?	come	fly in	altogether
.	.	0	1	2	3	4	5
6	7	8	9	10			

Remember
You may have to change the capital letters

• Check it •

Word Wall – At the zoo

Use these words to make up your own word problems.

monkeys 	snakes	bears	?

At the zoo	are	and	how many	animals

altogether	left	in total	There are	in

the cage	get out of the cage	.	.

one	two	three	four	five	six	seven	eight

nine	ten						

Remember
You may have to change the capital letters

• Check it •

Write It

Children are given illustrations and encouraged to write an appropriate word problem.
A word bank is provided for assistance.
The children are encouraged to check their work after completion.

Write It

My word problem

• Check it •

Word Bank

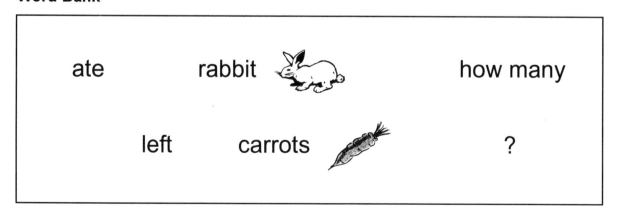

ate   rabbit   how many

left   carrots   ?

Write It

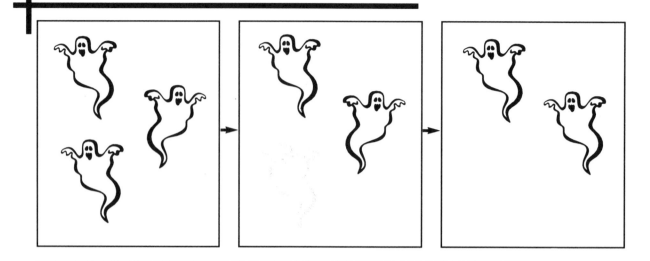

My word problem

• Check it •

Word Bank

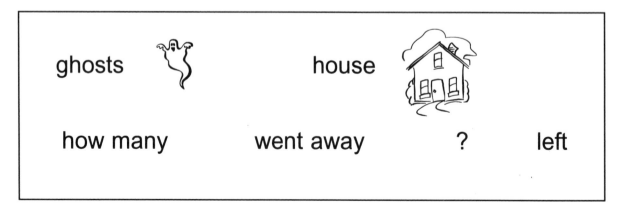

ghosts   house

how many   went away   ?   left

Write It

• Check it •

Word Bank

sweets	box	ate
left	?	how many

Write It

My word problem

• Check it •

Word Bank

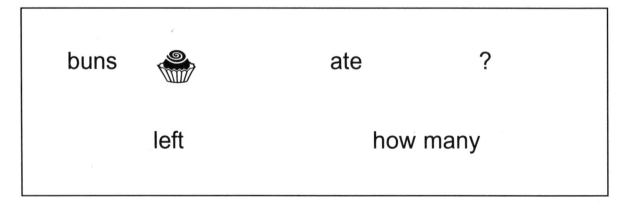

buns   ate   ?

left   how many

Write It

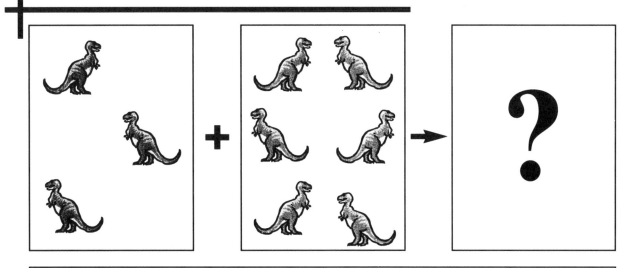

My word problem

• Check it •

Word Bank

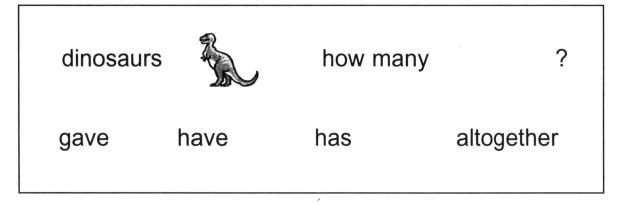

dinosaurs   how many   ?

gave   have   has   altogether

Write It

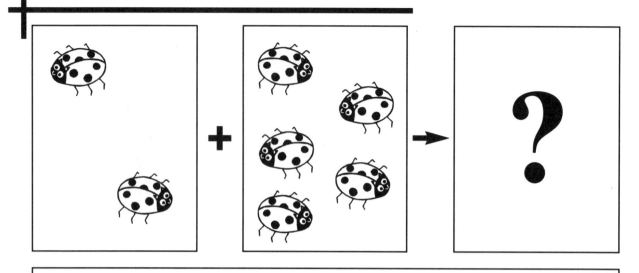

My word problem

• Check it •

Word Bank

ladybirds   in total   found

have   ?   how many

Write It

My word problem

• Check it •

Word Bank

cat   fish    how many

?   left   ate

Write It

My word problem

• Check it •

Word Bank

fish	🐟	more	bought	have
tank	altogether		boy	?

Draw and Write It

Children are given a horizontal, completed calculation and are asked to make appropriate illustrations. They are then encouraged to write their own word problems for the given calculation.
(Key Words and Word List can be used for assistance.)
Finally, they are encouraged to check their work.

Draw and Write It

$$4 + 4 = 8$$

Draw pictures for this calculation.

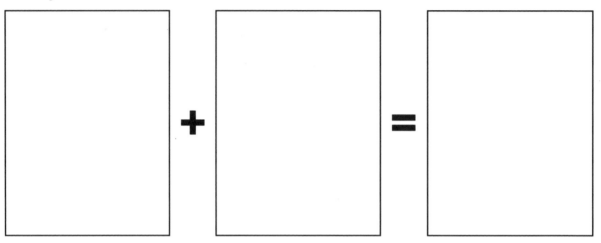

Write a word problem to go with it.
Use the Word List and Key Words.

• Check it •

Word Problems

Draw and Write It

9 + 1 = 10

Draw pictures for this calculation.

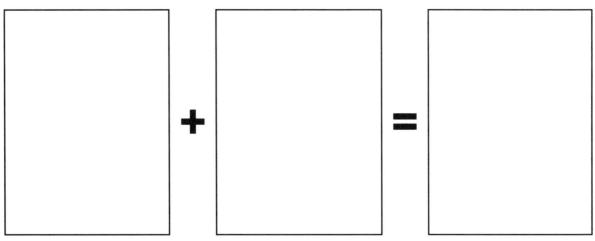

Write a word problem to go with it.
Use the Word List and Key Words.

• Check it •

Draw and Write It

2 + 1 = 3

Draw pictures for this calculation.

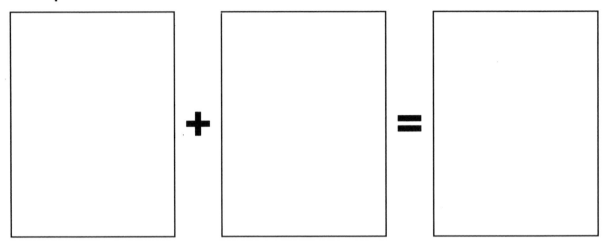

Write a word problem to go with it.
Use the Word List and Key Words.

My word problem

• Check it •

Draw and Write It

$$5 - 3 = 2$$

Draw pictures for this calculation.

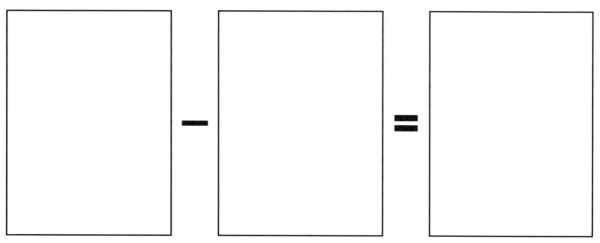

Write a word problem to go with it.
Use the Word List and Key Words.

• Check it •

Draw and Write It

$$8 - 4 = 4$$

Draw pictures for this calculation.

	−		=	

Write a word problem to go with it.
Use the Word List and Key Words.

My word problem

• Check it •

Why use Writing Frames?

The use of writing frames in literacy is well documented. They help the child focus his/her thoughts and give some guidance in what otherwise would be a blank page on which to write a story. In the past, mathematical word problems have simply been published with no guidance to the pupil as to what operation needs to be used in solving them. In the following pages there is a gradual introduction to the use of phrases which will help the pupil focus his or her thoughts on **'this problem is about ...'** and **'I have to find ...'**

This means that the pupil has to, if necessary, reread the original word problem to confirm that they understand what is being asked. These first worksheets use writing frames and multiple choice answers as 'scaffolding' which is gradually dismantled as the pupil becomes more competent. Earlier pages offer a multiple choice for the pupil to complete, whilst in later pages there is no multiple choice and the pupil has to write his/her own words to complete these sections.

The use of **'this means I have to ...'** and **'my estimate for the answer is ...'** used in conjunction with the symbol/language page (page 116) helps the pupil associate the mathematical symbols and operations with the correct mathematical language and, if desired, write the word beside the symbol on the worksheet, e.g. + **total**. Consistency with the language of problem solving is important.

'My estimate for the answer is ...'
The children should make an estimate of the answer before writing the calculation they think is correct to solve the problem. Having some idea of what the answer should be is an important mental facility and can help children see if their final calculation is correct or not. Have they made a procedural error which results in an answer so at variance with their estimate that we need to ask them 'Can you tell me what you were thinking when you did the working out?'

How can I check it?
(a) Is there any way of reworking the calculation to check the answer?
   e.g. 7+8 = 15; 8+7 = 15; 15-7 = 8; or 5 x 4 = 20; 4 x 5 = 20 reinforcing the use of associativity and commutativity.
(b) How did it match your estimate for the answer?

Here is the perfect opportunity to discuss and/or teach those mental strategies for the appropriate calculation, and possibly further word problems could be devised whereby the operation and the numbers focus upon a specific mental strategy.

We have deliberately omitted any problems that involve division. The mechanics of division are frequently the most difficult for children to understand and therefore would be a barrier to solving a problem involving such an operation. Word problems incorporating division could be written into future worksheets when the pupil has become more confident with the other operations and associated mathematical language.

Later pages leave the writing frames in place but omit the multiple choice aspect of the work, thus the pupil has to confirm what the problem is about by either writing in the space provided or telling the teacher.

Blank copies of problem solving formats are to be found at the back of the book (page 119) so that teachers can write personal word problems for individuals or groups and pupils can create their own personal word problems.

Crack It

Children are given a word problem and then guided to finding the main elements of that problem. Using the key words for assistance, they can decide if this word problem involves addition or subtraction. They are encouraged to estimate the answer, complete the calculation and then check it.

Crack It

Jack gave me 5 sweets . Lucy gave me 3 more.

How many sweets do I have altogether?

This problem is about

- butterflies
- sweets

I have to find

- sweets Lucy gave me
- sweets altogether

Key Words

+ _____ _____

− _____ _____

My estimate

My calculation

- More than 5

- Less than 5

• Check it •

Crack It

I buy 6 ice creams . I eat 4 ice creams .

How many are left?

This problem is about

- ice creams

- apples

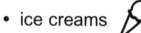

I have to find

- ice creams left

- ice creams in the shop

Key Words

+ _____   _____

− _____   _____

My estimate

My calculation

- More than 5

- Less than 5

• Check it •

Crack It

We saw 10 rockets . 5 rockets took off.

How many were left?

This problem is about

- rockets

- stars

I have to find

- rockets altogether

- rockets left

Key Words

+ _____   _____

− _____   _____

My estimate

My calculation

- More than 5

- Less than 5

• Check it •

Crack It

Jack put 5 cars  in the box.

Lucy put 4 cars in the box.

How many cars in total?

This problem is about

• boats

• cars

I have to find

• cars less than

• cars in total

Key Words

+ _____ _____

− _____ _____

My estimate

My calculation

• More than 5

• Less than 5

• Check it •

Crack It

9 spiders and 1 spider .

How many spiders altogether?

This problem is about

- spiders
- ladybirds

I have to find

- spiders less than
- spiders altogether

Key Words

+ _____ _____

– _____ _____

My estimate

My calculation

- More than 5

- Less than 5

• Check it •

Crack It

3 pencils ✏ on a desk. Jack put 3 pencils ✏ away.

How many are left?

This problem is about

- pencils
- books

I have to find

- pencils   left
- pencils   altogether

Key Words

\+ _____   _____

\− _____   _____

My estimate

My calculation

- More than 5
- Less than 5

• **Check it** •

Crack It

10 books on the desk. Jack put 3 books away.

How many are left?

This problem is about

- books
- pencils

I have to find

- books left
- books in total

Key Words

+ _____ _____

− _____ _____

My estimate

- More than 5
- Less than 5

My calculation

• Check it •

Crack It

3 ghosts in the house. 5 more ghosts come.

Altogether this makes?

This problem is about

- ghosts
- dinosaurs

I have to find

- ghosts left
- ghosts altogether

Key Words

+ _____ _____

− _____ _____

My estimate

- More than 5
- Less than 5

My calculation

• Check it •

Crack It

Jack has 6 dinosaurs . Lucy has 1 less than Jack.

How many dinosaurs does Lucy have?

This problem is about

•

I have to find

•

Key Words

+ _____   _____

− _____   _____

My estimate

My calculation

• More than 5

• Less than 5

• Check it •

Crack It

7 aeroplanes ✈ at the airport. 2 more aeroplanes ✈ come.

How many aeroplanes ✈ in total?

This problem is about

•

I have to find

•

Key Words

+ _____ _____

− _____ _____

My estimate

My calculation

• More than 5

• Less than 5

• Check it •

Crack It

8 boys fishing 🎣 . 5 boys go away.

How many are left?

This problem is about

•

I have to find

•

Key Words

\+ _____ _____

\- _____ _____

My estimate

My calculation

• More than 5

• Less than 5

• Check it •

Crack It

4 dinosaurs in the park. 3 more dinosaurs come.

How many altogether?

This problem is about

•

I have to find

•

Key Words

+ _____ _____

− _____ _____

 My estimate

 My calculation

• More than 5

• Less than 5

• Check it •

Crack It

4 children 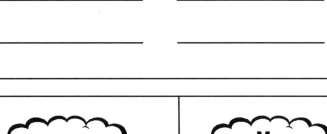 in the park. 2 more children  go into the park.

How many children in the park altogether?

This problem is about

•

I have to find

•

Key Words

+ _____ _____

− _____ _____

My estimate

My calculation

• More than 5

• Less than 5

• Check it •

Solve It

Children are given a word problem. They are encouraged to find the key words in the problem and decide whether to add, subtract or multiply in order to obtain the solution. Finally they complete the calculation and check it.

Solve It

There are 9 dinosaurs in the park. 3 dinosaurs go away.

How many are left in the park?

Key Words

+ —————————   —————————

− —————————   —————————

I have to   **+**

                 −

My calculation

• Check it •

Solve It

Jack gave me 6 sweets .
Lucy gave me 3 more sweets.

How many sweets do I have altogether?

Key Words

\+ —————————— ——————————

\- —————————— ——————————

I have to   **+**

−

My
calculation

• **Check it** •

Solve It

Jack found 3 spiders  .
Then he found 4 more spiders .

How many spiders does this make altogether?

Key Words

+ ——————————   ——————————

− ——————————   ——————————

I have to   **+**

−

My
calculation

• Check it •

Solve It

Jack has 6 fish  in his tank. A big cat eats 4 fish.

How many are left?

Key Words

\+ _____   _____

\− _____   _____

I have to   **+**

−

My calculation

• Check it •

Solve It

I have 5 sandwiches  for lunch.

I eat 2 sandwiches  .

How many are left?

Key Words

+ _____ _____

− _____ _____

I have to   **+**

−

My calculation

• Check it •

Solve It

There are 8 children 🧒🧒 on a red bus.
When the bus stops 3 children 🧒🧒 get off.

How many children are left on the red bus?

Key Words

+ ——————————— ———————————

− ——————————— ———————————

I have to   **+**

−

My
calculation

• Check it •

Solve It

David has 10 apples. Mollie has 15 apples.

How many apples altogether?

This problem is about

oranges _____

apples _____

pears _____

I have to find

- **How old David is** ☐
- **Mollie's favourite colour** ☐
- **The number of apples altogether** ☐

This means I have to

+ ☐

− ☐

X ☐

My estimate for the answer is

between 10 and 20 ☐

between 20 and 40 ☐

between 40 and 50 ☐

Here is my calculation

How can I check it?

Solve It

In a tree there are 9 sparrows, 12 blackbirds and 2 owls.

What is the total number of birds in the tree?

This problem is about

birds   _____

mice   _____

rabbits   _____

I have to find

• **How many trees there are** ☐

• **The number of birds altogether** ☐

• **How tall the tree is** ☐

This means I have to

+ ☐

− ☐

X ☐

My estimate for the answer is

between 10 and 20 ☐

between 20 and 40 ☐

between 40 and 50 ☐

Here is my calculation

How can I check it?

Solve It

I have 12 coloured pens. My sister has 6 and my brother has 10.

How many coloured pens altogether?

This problem is about

rulers _____

coloured pens _____

pencil sharpeners _____

I have to find

• **My sister's favourite colour** ☐

• **The total number of coloured pens** ☐

• **The cost of a ruler** ☐

This means I have to

+ ☐

– ☐

X ☐

My estimate for the answer is

between 10 and 20 ☐

between 20 and 40 ☐

between 40 and 50 ☐

Here is my calculation

How can I check it?

Solve It

For a children's party 14 tins of cola, 12 tins of orange and
8 tins of lemonade were bought.

How many tins were bought altogether?

This problem is about

birthdays _____

parties _____

soft drinks _____

I have to find

- **How many candles are on the cake** ☐
- **The total number of soft drinks bought** ☐
- **How many children were at the party** ☐

This means I have to

+ ☐

− ☐

X ☐

My estimate for the answer is

between 10 and 20 ☐

between 20 and 40 ☐

between 40 and 50 ☐

Here is my calculation

How can I check it?

Solve It

My friends have caught chicken pox. Kate has 11 spots,
Peter has 7 spots, and Anansi has 14 spots.

How many spots are there altogether?

This problem is about

spots on faces _____

a broken leg _____

a sore head _____

I have to find

• **Who has the most spots** ☐

• **Who got the spots first** ☐

• **The total number of spots** ☐

This means I have to

+ ☐

– ☐

X ☐

My estimate for the answer is

between 10 and 20 ☐

between 20 and 40 ☐

between 40 and 50 ☐

Here is my calculation

How can I check it?

Solve It

In a garage there are 12 red cars, 4 blue cars and 6 white cars.

How many cars are there altogether?

This problem is about

colours _____

bicycles _____

cars _____

I have to find

• **The fastest car** ☐

• **How many wheels on a car** ☐

• **The total number of cars** ☐

This means I have to

+ ☐

− ☐

X ☐

My estimate for the answer is

between 10 and 20 ☐

between 20 and 40 ☐

between 40 and 50 ☐

Here is my calculation

How can I check it?

Solve It

There are 21 slices in a loaf of bread. I use 4 slices to make a packed lunch.

How many slices of bread are left?

This problem is about

beef burgers _____

slices of bread _____

buns _____

I have to find

• **How many slices of bread are left** ☐

• **The cost of a loaf of bread** ☐

• **How many sandwiches fit in my lunchbox** ☐

This means I have to

+ ☐

− ☐

X ☐

My estimate for the answer is

between 10 and 20 ☐

between 20 and 40 ☐

between 40 and 50 ☐

Here is my calculation

How can I check it?

Solve It

The school has 30 bean bags, but 6 are torn and are thrown away.

How many are left?

This problem is about

sports day _____

bean bags _____

baked beans _____

I have to find

- **Who likes baked beans** ☐

- **How many bean bags are left** ☐

- **When sports day is** ☐

This means I have to

+ ☐

− ☐

X ☐

My estimate for the answer is

between 10 and 20 ☐

between 20 and 40 ☐

between 40 and 50 ☐

Here is my calculation

How can I check it?

Solve It

There are 48 Easter eggs in a box. 16 are eaten.

How many are left?

This problem is about

ice cream _____

Easter eggs _____

crisps _____

I have to find

• **How many flavours of crisps there are** ☐

• **How many Easter eggs are left** ☐

• **How many boxes I can carry** ☐

This means I have to

+ ☐

− ☐

X ☐

My estimate for the answer is

between 10 and 20 ☐

between 20 and 40 ☐

between 40 and 50 ☐

Here is my calculation

How can I check it?

Solve It

My house number is 37. Abdul lives at number 22.

What is the difference between these numbers?

This problem is about

street names _____

house numbers _____

Coronation Street _____

I have to find

- **The house number next door** ☐

- **The last house number in the street** ☐

- **How much bigger my house number is than Abdul's** ☐

This means I have to

+ ☐

− ☐

X ☐

My estimate for the answer is

between 10 and 20 ☐

between 20 and 40 ☐

between 40 and 50 ☐

Here is my calculation

How can I check it?

Solve It

Last year Janice read 9 books and Susan read 20.

How many more books did Susan read than Janice?

This problem is about

school   _____

books   _____

boys   _____

I have to find

- **What time school starts** ☐
- **The cost of a book** ☐
- **How many more books Susan read than Janice** ☐

This means I have to

+ ☐

− ☐

X ☐

My estimate for the answer is

between 10 and 20 ☐

between 20 and 40 ☐

between 40 and 50 ☐

Here is my calculation

How can I check it?

Solve It

An ice cream costs 90p, but I have only got 45p.

How much more money do I need to buy one?

This problem is about

drinks _____

crisps _____

ice cream _____

I have to find

• **How much a lollipop costs** ☐

• **How much more money I need to buy an ice cream** ☐

• **How many pennies in £1** ☐

This means I have to

+ ☐

− ☐

X ☐

My estimate for the answer is

between 10 and 20 ☐

between 20 and 40 ☐

between 40 and 50 ☐

Here is my calculation

How can I check it?

Solve It

An egg-box holds 6 eggs.

How many eggs will 3 boxes hold?

This problem is about

chickens _____

eggs _____

ducks _____

I have to find

- **How many eggs in 3 boxes** ☐
- **The weight of an egg** ☐
- **How long it takes to boil an egg** ☐

This means I have to

+ ☐

– ☐

X ☐

My estimate for the answer is

between 10 and 20 ☐

between 20 and 40 ☐

between 40 and 50 ☐

<u>Here is my calculation</u>

How can I check it?

Solve It

A tray of soft drinks holds 6 cans.

How many drinks would 5 trays hold?

This problem is about

tea _____

soft drinks _____

coffee _____

I have to find

- **The cost of a soft drink** ☐
- **How quickly I can drink a can of soft drink** ☐
- **How many soft drinks 5 trays will hold** ☐

This means I have to

+ ☐

– ☐

X ☐

My estimate for the answer is

between 10 and 20 ☐

between 20 and 40 ☐

between 40 and 50 ☐

Here is my calculation

How can I check it?

Solve It

A triangle has 3 sides.

How many sides will 9 triangles have?

This problem is about

squares   _____

cubes   _____

triangles   _____

I have to find

• **How many sides on 9 squares**   ☐

• **How to draw a circle**   ☐

• **How many sides on 9 triangles** ☐

This means I have to

+ ☐

− ☐

X ☐

My estimate for the answer is

between 10 and 20 ☐

between 20 and 40 ☐

between 40 and 50 ☐

Here is my calculation

How can I check it?

Solve It

A ladybird has 7 spots on its back.

How many spots will 4 ladybirds have?

This problem is about

spiders _____

ladybirds _____

fish _____

I have to find

• **How many spots on dice** ☐

• **How fast a ladybird can crawl** ☐

• **How many spots on 4 ladybirds** ☐

This means I have to

+ ☐

− ☐

X ☐

My estimate for the answer is

between 10 and 20 ☐

between 20 and 40 ☐

between 40 and 50 ☐

Here is my calculation

How can I check it?

Solve It

There are 4 bananas in a bunch.

How many bananas would be on 5 bunches?

This problem is about

coconuts _____

bananas _____

oranges _____

I have to find

• **How many pips in an orange** ☐

• **The cost of a bunch of bananas** ☐

• **How many bananas on 5 bunches** ☐

This means I have to

+ ☐

− ☐

X ☐

My estimate for the answer is

between 10 and 20 ☐

between 20 and 40 ☐

between 40 and 50 ☐

<u>**Here is my calculation**</u>

How can I check it?

Solve It

23 cyclists take part in a race.

How many bicycle wheels are there?

This problem is about

cars   _____

buses   _____

bicycle wheels   _____

I have to find

• **Who won the race** ☐

• **The cost of a bicycle** ☐

• **The total number of bicycle wheels** ☐

This means I have to

+ ☐

− ☐

X ☐

My estimate for the answer is

between 10 and 20 ☐

between 20 and 40 ☐

between 40 and 50 ☐

<u>Here is my calculation</u>

How can I check it?

Solve It

Victoria has 11 chips on her plate. Jordan has 12 chips and Jackie has 14 chips.

How many chips are there altogether?

This problem is about

I have to find

This means I have to

+ ☐

− ☐

X ☐

My estimate for the answer is

between 10 and 20 ☐

between 20 and 40 ☐

between 40 and 50 ☐

Here is my calculation

How can I check it?

Solve It

Robyn has 16 toy dinosaurs, 4 toy sharks and 7 toy snakes.

How many toy animals does she have altogether?

This problem is about

I have to find

This means I have to

+ ☐

− ☐

X ☐

My estimate for the answer is

between 10 and 20 ☐

between 20 and 40 ☐

between 40 and 50 ☐

Here is my calculation

How can I check it?

Solve It

In a fruit salad I use 4 oranges, 5 apples,
12 strawberries and 8 plums.

How many pieces of fruit do I use altogether?

This problem is about

I have to find

This means I have to

+ ☐

− ☐

X ☐

My estimate for the answer is

between 10 and 20 ☐

between 20 and 40 ☐

between 40 and 50 ☐

Here is my calculation

How can I check it?

Solve It

In my class 16 children have brown hair, 7 have blonde hair and 4 have black hair.

How many children are there in the class altogether?

This problem is about

I have to find

This means I have to

+ ☐

− ☐

X ☐

My estimate for the answer is

between 10 and 20 ☐

between 20 and 40 ☐

between 40 and 50 ☐

Here is my calculation

How can I check it?

Solve It

I am 12 years old, my brother is 7 years old and my sister is 8 years old.

What is the total of our ages?

This problem is about

I have to find

This means I have to

+ ☐

− ☐

X ☐

My estimate for the answer is

between 10 and 20 ☐

between 20 and 40 ☐

between 40 and 50 ☐

Here is my calculation

How can I check it?

Solve It

A farmer has 12 sheep, 9 cows and 6 ducks.

How many animals does he have altogether?

This problem is about

I have to find

This means I have to

+ ☐

− ☐

X ☐

My estimate for the answer is

between 10 and 20 ☐

between 20 and 40 ☐

between 40 and 50 ☐

Here is my calculation

How can I check it?

Solve It

In a spelling test of 35 words I got 6 wrong.

How many words did I get right?

This problem is about

☑ ☑ ✗ ☑
☑ ✗ ☑ ✗

I have to find

This means I have to

+ ☐

− ☐

X ☐

My estimate for the answer is

between 10 and 20 ☐

between 20 and 40 ☐

between 40 and 50 ☐

Here is my calculation

How can I check it?

Solve It

There are 35 chips in a carton. I eat 7 of them.

How many chips are left?

This problem is about

I have to find

This means I have to

+ ☐

− ☐

X ☐

My estimate for the answer is

between 10 and 20 ☐

between 20 and 40 ☐

between 40 and 50 ☐

Here is my calculation

How can I check it?

Solve It

On a set of ladders there are 30 steps. 7 are broken.

How many are still safe?

This problem is about

I have to find

This means I have to

+ ☐

− ☐

X ☐

My estimate for the answer is

between 10 and 20 ☐

between 20 and 40 ☐

between 40 and 50 ☐

Here is my calculation

How can I check it?

Solve It

There are 27 cars in a race and 12 crash.

How many are left in the race?

This problem is about

I have to find

This means I have to

+ ☐
− ☐
X ☐

My estimate for the answer is

between 10 and 20 ☐

between 20 and 40 ☐

between 40 and 50 ☐

Here is my calculation

How can I check it?

Solve It

I buy a box of 40 tea bags and use 16.

How many tea bags are left?

This problem is about

I have to find

This means I have to

+ ☐

− ☐

X ☐

My estimate for the answer is

between 10 and 20 ☐

between 20 and 40 ☐

between 40 and 50 ☐

Here is my calculation

How can I check it?

Solve It

There are 24 cups in a tea-set and 6 are broken.

How many are left?

This problem is about

I have to find

This means I have to

+ ☐
− ☐
X ☐

My estimate for the answer is

between 10 and 20 ☐

between 20 and 40 ☐

between 40 and 50 ☐

<u>Here is my calculation</u>

How can I check it?

Solve It

I need to set the table for 6 people. Each person needs a knife, a fork and a spoon.

How many pieces of cutlery are needed altogether?

This problem is about

I have to find

This means I have to

+ ☐

− ☐

X ☐

My estimate for the answer is

between 10 and 20 ☐

between 20 and 40 ☐

between 40 and 50 ☐

Here is my calculation

How can I check it?

Solve It

My mum bakes some buns. She bakes them in rows of 6
with 4 buns in each row.

How many buns does she bake?

This problem is about

I have to find

This means I have to

+ ☐

− ☐

X ☐

My estimate for the answer is

between 10 and 20 ☐

between 20 and 40 ☐

between 40 and 50 ☐

Here is my calculation

How can I check it?

Solve It

There are 8 sausages in a packet.

How many sausages are there in 5 packets?

This problem is about

I have to find

This means I have to

+ ☐

− ☐

X ☐

My estimate for the answer is

between 10 and 20 ☐

between 20 and 40 ☐

between 40 and 50 ☐

Here is my calculation

How can I check it?

Solve It

A spider has 8 legs.

How many legs do 4 spiders have?

This problem is about

I have to find

This means I have to

+ ☐

− ☐

X ☐

My estimate for the answer is

between 10 and 20 ☐

between 20 and 40 ☐

between 40 and 50 ☐

Here is my calculation

How can I check it?

Solve It

A chair has 4 legs.

How many legs do 8 chairs have?

This problem is about

I have to find

This means I have to

+ ☐

− ☐

X ☐

My estimate for the answer is

between 10 and 20 ☐

between 20 and 40 ☐

between 40 and 50 ☐

<u>Here is my calculation</u>

How can I check it?

Solve It

There are 11 players in a football team.

How many players are there in 4 teams?

This problem is about

I have to find

This means I have to

+ ☐

− ☐

X ☐

My estimate for the answer is

between 10 and 20 ☐

between 20 and 40 ☐

between 40 and 50 ☐

<u>Here is my calculation</u>

How can I check it?

GAMES

1. ZOOM

Objective   To give children oral practice making their own word problems.

Number of players   2 – 4 players.

Materials   1 baseboard (A3 size).
(see pages 106 — 110)   2 – 4 coloured counters.
          1 set of cards (cut out and laminated, if possible).

Rules

1. The cards are shuffled and placed face down on the table.

2. The player to the left of the person shuffling the cards starts.

3. The first player takes a card from the pile.

4. The player reads the card and then makes up a word problem. The Word List may be used for help.

5. The other players decide if the word problem is sensible.

6. If the word problem is sensible then the player moves his/her counter as directed.

7. The next player picks up a card.

8. If a player lands on a 'Car' card must be picked up.

9. If a player picks up a 'Pit Stop' card, the player misses a turn.

10. The winner is the player to finish first.

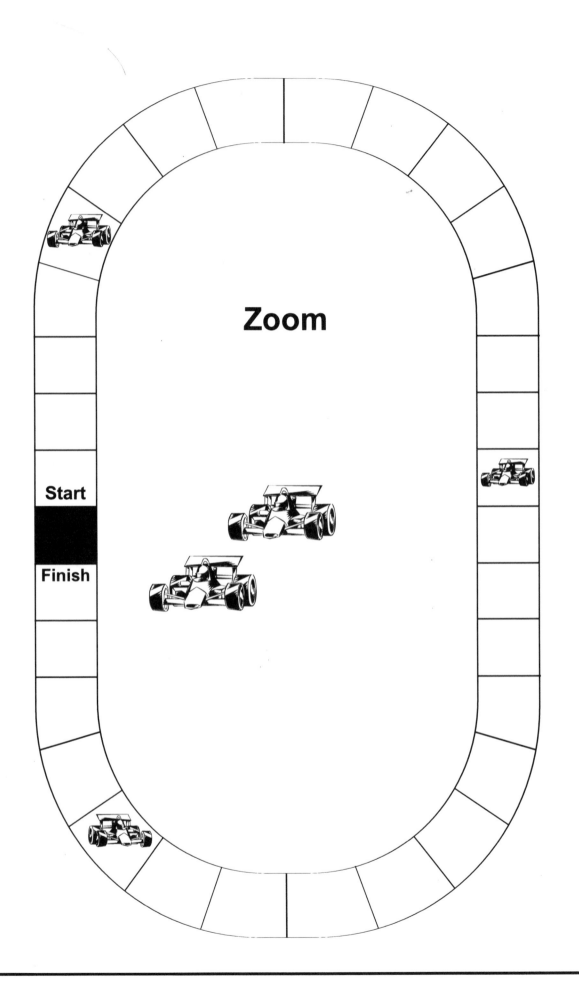

Zoom

Start

Finish

Make your own word problem

Make your own word problem

Make your own word problem

Pit Stop

Need to refuel

Miss a turn

Pit Stop

Started to rain – change tyres

Miss a turn

Pit Stop

Problem with engine

Miss a turn

7 – 3

Forward 3

10 – 6

Forward 3

8 + 1

Forward 3

3 + 5

Forward 3

7 + 3

Forward 3

8 – 6

Forward 3

He ate 3 sandwiches

Forward 2

5 boats sail away

Forward 2

The big cat ate 4 fish

Forward 2

How many snakes altogether?

Forward 2

7 birds fly away

Forward 2

I have 9 ladybirds

Forward 2

Lucy buys 8 ice creams

Forward 2

10 children on the red bus

Forward 2

There are 5 black spiders in the house

Forward 2

Jack has 4 footballs

Forward 2

Jack has 9 books

Forward 2

How many are left?

Forward 2

There are 8 birds **Forward 2**	**6 monsters run away** **Forward 2**
7 rockets take off **Forward 2**	**If there are 9 buns** **on a plate** **Forward 2**
7 children at the bus stop **Forward 2**	**Jack eats 7 sandwiches** **Forward 2**
How many altogether? **Forward 2**	**How many are left?** **Forward 2**
Lucy has 1 pencil **Forward 2**	**How many in total?** **Forward 2**

How many are left?

Forward 2

How many monsters in total?

Forward 2

How many fish altogether?

Forward 2

Jack got 2 more rabbits

Forward 2

Mollie has 6 dinosaurs

Forward 2

There are 5 butterflies in a garden

Forward 2

Asha has 9 sweets

Forward 2

6 aeroplanes fly away

Forward 2

How many are left?

Forward 2

There are 2 bears and 8 snakes in the zoo

Forward 2

Word Problems

2. LOOP CARDS

Each set of 8 cards is 'self-checking'. The answers to the word problem in one card are to be found in the circle of another card. The cards therefore, form a 'loop' with the word problem on the last card matching the answer of the first card chosen. The cards can either be laid in a straight line or a circle as illustrated.

Teachers can use blank loop cards on the resources pages to write their own sets, matching the ability and progress of the children, or pupils can write sets for each other.

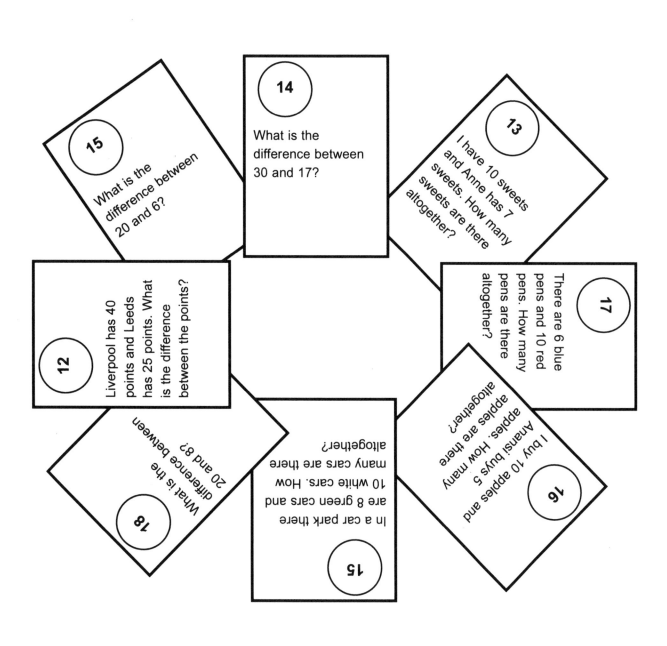

12 Liverpool has 40 points and Leeds has 31 points. What is the difference between the points?

13 I have 10 sweets and Abdul has 7 sweets. How many sweets altogether?

9 What is the difference between 20 and 6?

17 There are 6 blue and 10 red pens. How many pens altogether?

18 What is the difference between 20 and 8?

15 In a car park there are 8 green cars and 10 white cars. How many cars are there altogether?

14 What is the difference between 30 and 17?

16 I buy 10 apples and Peter buys 5 apples. How many apples are there altogether?

Word Problems

15 By how much is 30 bigger than 17?

14 What is the total of 5, 7 and 3?

30 By how much is 20 bigger than 6?

5 What is the total of 21 and 9?

22 By how much is 19 bigger than 14?

11 What is the total of 9, 7 and 6?

25 By how much is 27 bigger than 16?

13 What is the total of 10, 6 and 9?

26 What is 18 take away 12?

6 What is 19 take away 6?

18 What is 17 take away 5?

27 What is 20 take away 3?

13 If I add 21 and 8, what is the total?

12 If I add 14 and 12, what is the total?

29 If I add 16 and 11, what is the total?

17 If I add 13 and 5, what is the total?

Word Problems

RESOURCE
SHEETS

Key Words

Addition Words

+

add

makes

and   total

more   altogether

Subtraction Words

−

less

away

take away   less than

left   leaves

Word List

aeroplane

apple

bag

bear

boat

book

box

bun

bus

bus stop

butterfly

car

carrot

cat

children

dinosaur

fish

football

Word List

ghost	house	ice cream
ladybird	monkey	pencil
rabbit	rocket	sandwich
snake	spider	sweet
swing		

Word List

Make a Word Problem

1	2	3

Put in order

1
2
3

Cut and Paste

Draw It

Cut and Paste

Put in order

1	
2	
3	

• Check it •

Draw pictures for this calculation

Cut and Paste It

My word
problem

• Check it •

Word Bank

Write It

My word problem

• Check it •

Word Bank

Draw and Write It

Draw pictures for this calculation.

Write a word problem to go with it.
Use the Word List and Key Words.

• **Check it** •

Crack It

This problem is about

•

I have to find

•

Key Words

+ _____ _____

− _____ _____

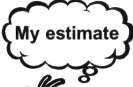 My estimate

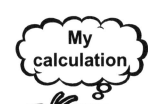 My calculation

• More than 5

• Less than 5

• Check it •

Solve It

Key Words

+ _____ _____

− _____ _____

I have to   **+**

−

My
calculation

• Check it •

Solve It

This problem is about

- _____

- _____

- _____

I have to find

- ☐

- ☐

- ☐

This means I have to

+ ☐

− ☐

X ☐

My estimate for the answer is

between 10 and 20 ☐

between 20 and 40 ☐

between 40 and 50 ☐

Here is my calculation

How can I check it?

Solve It

This problem is about

- _____

I have to find

-

This means I have to		My estimate for the answer is	
+	☐	between 10 and 20	☐
−	☐	between 20 and 40	☐
X	☐	between 40 and 50	☐

Here is my calculation

How can I check it?

Word Problems

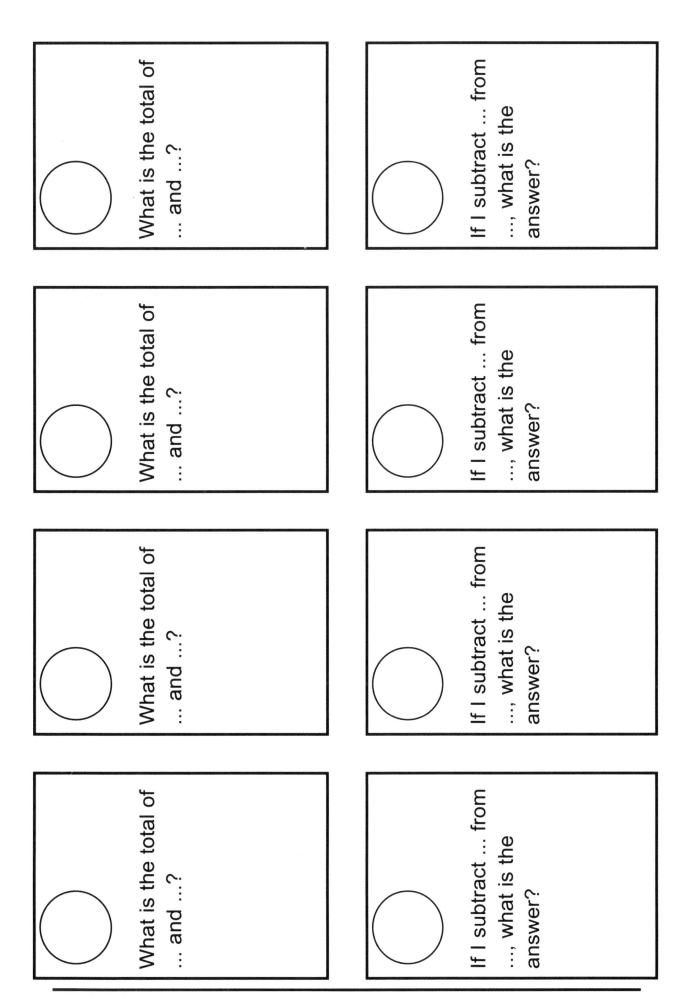

What is the total of
... and ...?

What is the total of
... and ...?

What is the total of
... and ...?

What is the total of
... and ...?

If I subtract ... from
..., what is the
answer?

If I subtract ... from
..., what is the
answer?

If I subtract ... from
..., what is the
answer?

If I subtract ... from
..., what is the
answer?

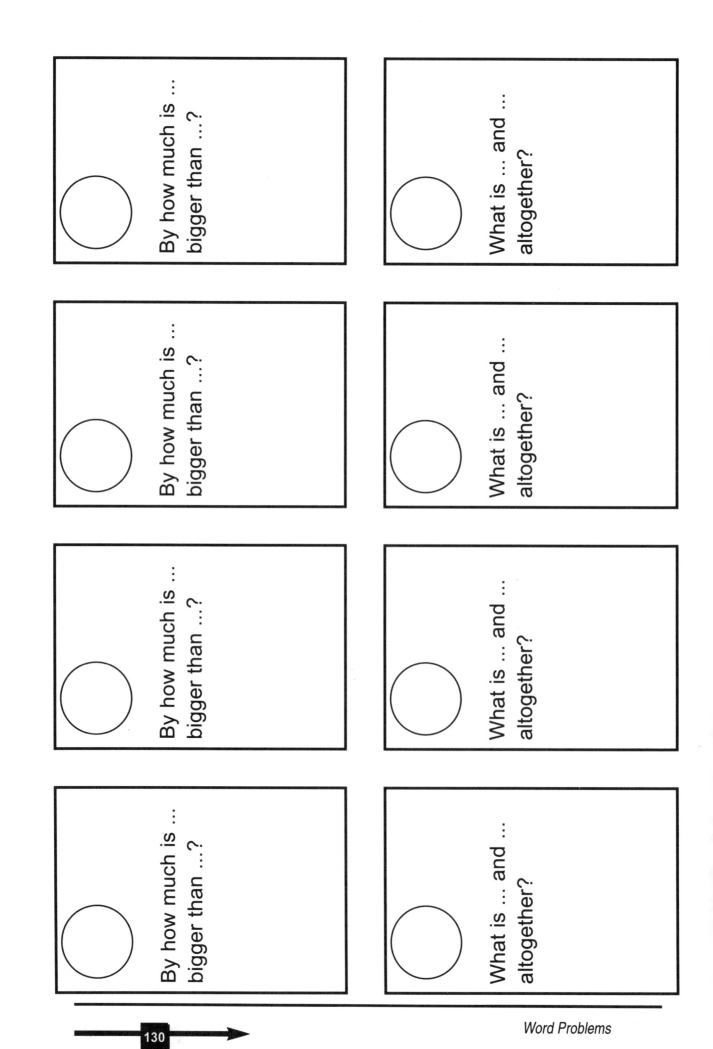

By how much is ... bigger than ...?

By how much is ... bigger than ...?

By how much is ... bigger than ...?

By how much is ... bigger than ...?

What is ... and ... altogether?

What is ... and ... altogether?

What is ... and ... altogether?

What is ... and ... altogether?

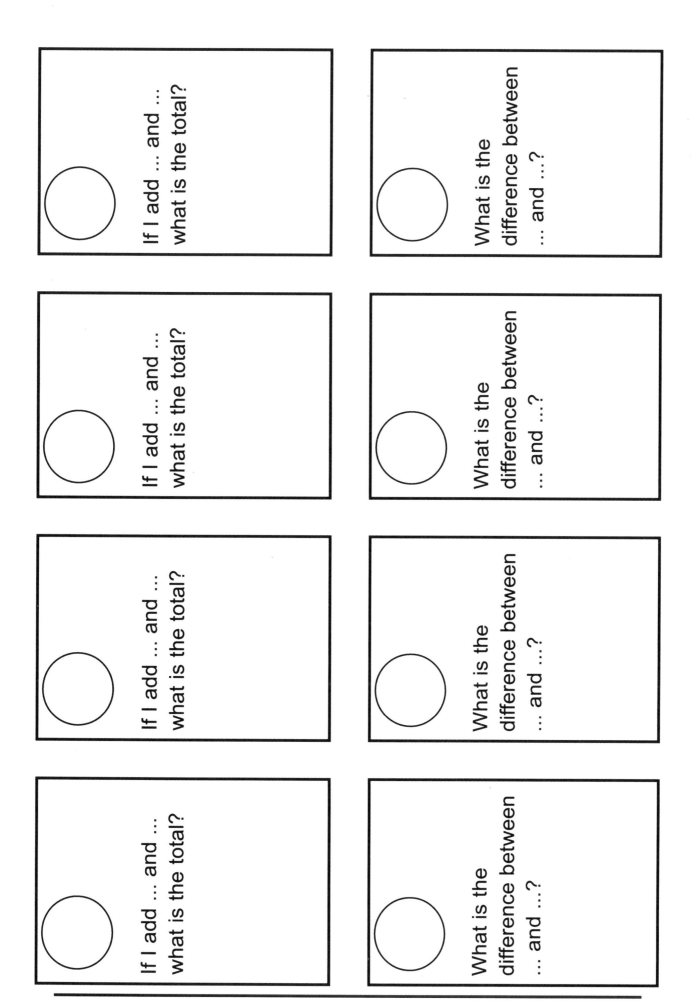

If I add ... and ...
what is the total?

If I add ... and ...
what is the total?

If I add ... and ...
what is the total?

If I add ... and ...
what is the total?

What is the
difference between
... and ...?

What is the
difference between
... and ...?

What is the
difference between
... and ...?

What is the
difference between
... and ...?